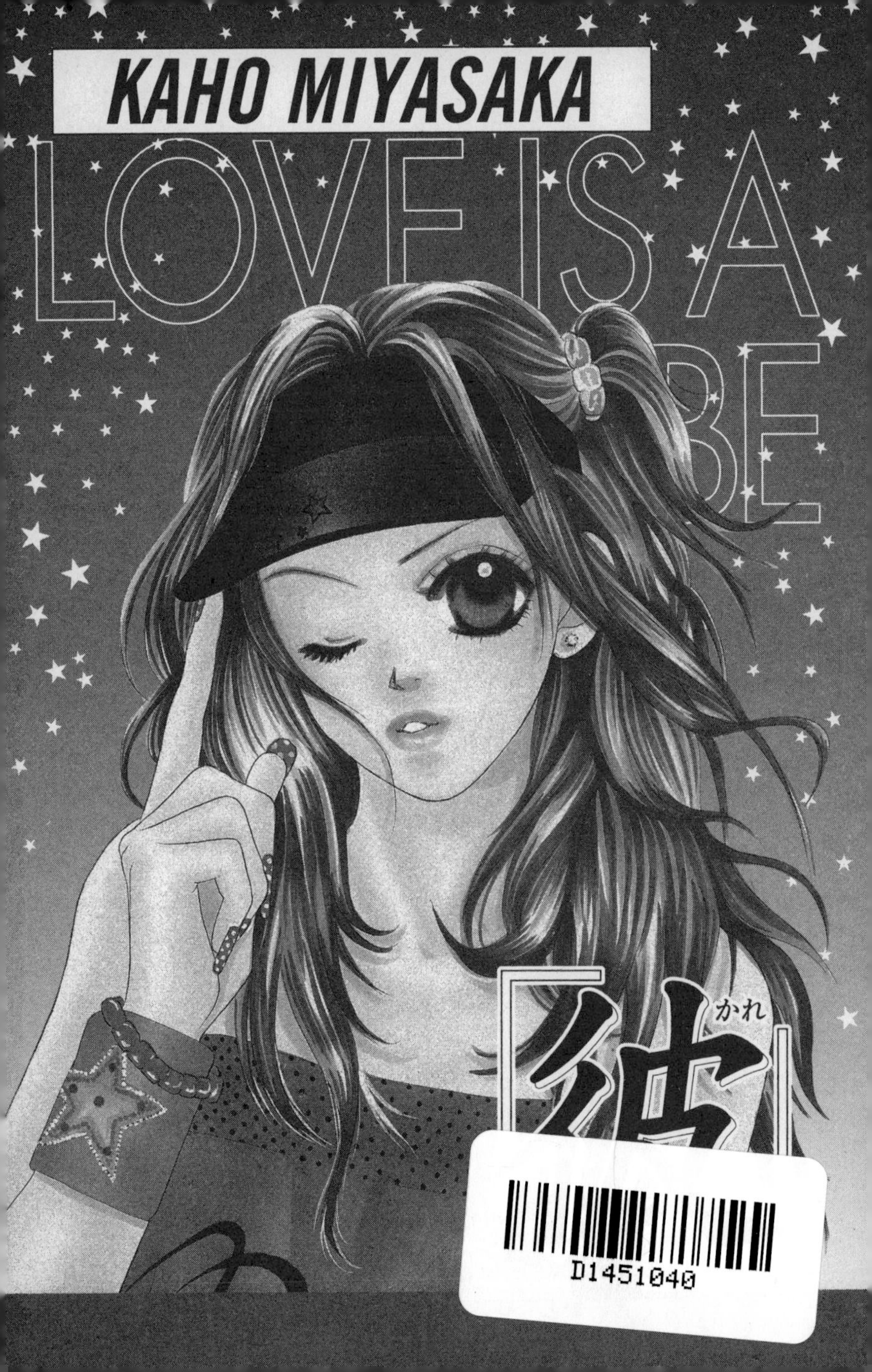
KAHO MIYASAKA
LOVE IS A
BE
彼
かれ

Characters and Story Digest

Karin Karino

A freshman at a girls' prep school. Karin wasn't very interested in boys, until she met...

Aoi Kiriya

An amateur photographer and a student at a nearby boys' school.

KARE First Love

5

Karin went to an all-girls' school because she was never comfortable around boys. It might not have been bliss, but she managed.

Everything changed when she met Kiriya on the morning bus. Her classmate, Yuka, tried to sabotage them, but with Nanri's support, Karin and Kiriya started going out.

For their first summer vacation together, the two planned a trip to Okinawa with their friends. They stayed on the beach near the spot where Kiriya's brother had drowned. It was an emotional trip, of course, but it brought Karin and Kiriya closer. They spent the night together, but Karin was so nervous that she drank too much...and the vacation ended with Karin's virginity intact.

Karin's father became convinced that Kiriya was a bad influence, and he forbade the two from seeing each other. But on Christmas Eve, Kiriya called on Karin in secret, and now they find themselves alone in Karin's room at midnight...

Nanri Ayase

Karin's classmate. She recently broke up with her married boyfriend.

Shoko Akiba

The widow of Kiriya's older brother, the famous photographer Yuji.

Hiromu & Tohru

Kiriya's friends. Hiromu's cool. Tohru's girl-crazy.

Message From the Author

Lately I've been getting more mail from male readers, which I found quite surprising at first. But then I found out that there were many reasons for this, such as their "sister was reading it," or a "female friend told them to read it," or some of their "female classmates made them read it." (laughs) And the most common reason was that their "girlfriends told them to read it." Probably most of the girls out there who told their boyfriends to read this comic would like their boyfriends to be a bit like Kiriya. Good luck guys...

SMACK.

WAIT.

I...
I'M A
LITTLE
...

•••••

OW...

...OUCH.

OH..

I'M
SORRY.

11

12

I'M NOT "USED TO" THIS, KARIN...

YOU DID THIS TO ME...

Was that normal...?

It seemed weird...

Did I make that sound...

Could Kiriya hear it...?

It didn't even sound like me...

Was...

Was that me...?

NO... NO, IT'S OKAY...

I'M SORRY... JUST WHEN YOU WERE GETTING INTO IT...

At least I can catch my breath for a minute...

OH. THAT...

I...

UM...

I HAVE...

"TAKE THIS..."

"MAKE SURE YOU'RE PROTECTED, OKAY?"

...

KIND OF A LETDOWN, HUH?

Kiriya...

...

Won't it seem strange...?

Like I was planning it or something. Will he think that's weird...?

17

KNOCK
KNOCK

YOU STILL UP?

KARIN?

OKAY, BUT DON'T STAY UP TOO LATE.

OKAY...

YEAH...

I'M GONNA READ A LITTLE BEFORE I GO TO SLEEP...

Oh, crap.

IF THAT HAD BEEN YOUR DAD...

I'D BE DEAD BY NOW.

.....

...THAT WAS *CLOSE.*

THIS IS KIND OF SAD...

SIGH

.....

21

I...

KARIN, I'M SO SORRY...

I'M SORRY...

...I CAN DO THIS.

NO, I'M FINE...

I WAS JUST SURPRISED, THAT'S ALL. I'M OKAY... I...

I SCARED YOU...

NO...

...WE CAN STOP HERE FOR TONIGHT.

30

UH-HUH...

YEAH, BUT...

CAN I OPEN IT?

I DROPPED IT AND--

...SURE.

THANK YOU. THIS MUST HAVE BEEN EXPENSIVE...

WOW...

A SILVER KEY RING.

RUSTLE

I HOPE YOU LIKE WHAT I GOT YOU.

This
is from
that day
at the
drugstore
...

I KNOW YOUR EARS AREN'T PIERCED YET, BUT...

I THOUGHT THESE WOULD LOOK NICE ON YOU.

MAYBE YOU COULD WEAR THEM SOMETIME WHEN WE'RE TOGETHER...

...YOU REMEM-BERED.

OF COURSE. I REMEMBER EVERYTHING ABOUT YOU...

This is our first Christmas together...

His present got smashed...

And then...

KARIN
?

......

HEY, WHY ARE YOU CRYING?

WHAT'S WRONG?

YOU'RE ALWAYS SO GOOD TO ME, AND I WANT TO MAKE YOU HAPPY, BUT...

I CAN'T EVEN HAVE SEX RIGHT...

WE...

WE DIDN'T DO IT...

NOT YET... DON'T...

.....

STAY A LITTLE BIT LONGER... PLEASE?

41

THAT'S THE FIRST TIME I'VE EVER HEARD YOU SAY THAT.

...I LIKE THE SOUND OF IT.

HEH HEH

UM...

NOTHING.

STOP MOVING AROUND SO MUCH...

HUH ?

WHAT IS IT?

OH...

UH-OH...

DOWN, BOY...

I LOVE THIS. ♡

THINK ABOUT SOMETHING ELSE...

CHILL. CHILL. BE COOL...

I love how we fit together...

WOW...

HE GAVE YOU *TWO* PRESENTS?

I KNOW, RIGHT...?

WHOA...

THESE LOOK EXPENSIVE...

THE EARRINGS...

YOU GUYS WERE ALL LOVEY-DOVEY ON CHRISTMAS, RIGHT?

OH, DON'T. KIRIYA LIKED IT, SO IT'S FINE. I MEAN, IT'S NOT A COMPETITION, YOU KNOW?

THE THING I GAVE KIRIYA WASN'T AS NICE. I FEEL BAD ABOUT THAT.

ERM...?!

DID YOU DO IT? DID YOU LIKE IT?

YEAH, I MEAN, WELL SURE, BUT...

Then I got so scared that I freaked out Kiriya and we had to stop...

WELL... I MEAN, IT REALLY HURT...

SO YOU DID DO IT?!

CONGRATULATIONS.

NANRI...

DID IT HURT YOUR FIRST TIME?

I can't tell her that it didn't happen. It's too embarrassing...

UH...

WELL...

I KNOW, RIGHT? IT'S KIND OF WEIRD AT FIRST.

I DIDN'T KNOW MY HIPS WOULD STRETCH THAT FAR...

•••••

HA HA HA...

ACTUALLY, IT WAS OKAY MY FIRST TIME-- BUT DON'T WORRY. IT'LL FEEL BETTER AFTER A WHILE.

WH-WHAT?!

ULP

WHOOA...

I wonder if I'm weird for messing up like I did...?

Nanri did okay her first time...

•••

46

THESE ARE *DIAMONDS...*

I THOUGHT THEY WERE CUBIC ZIRCONIA AT FIRST, BUT THESE ARE REAL.

HE WANTS TO SHOW EVERYONE THAT YOU'RE TOGETHER. I MEAN, YOU DON'T EVEN HAVE PIERCED EARS, RIGHT?

OH! MAYBE IT'S A TEST! LIKE, "IF YOU LOVE ME, THEN PIERCE YOUR EARS."

I'M KIDDING...

KIRIYA MUST REALLY BE SERIOUS ABOUT YOU.

...SERIOUSLY?

YEP.

THEY'RE SMALL, BUT I BET THEY COST AT LEAST ¥20,000 OR ¥30,000* ...

47

*ROUGHLY $185-$277

Kiriya...

Did you work extra hours just to buy these...?

I should pierce my ears...

Since I messed up the sex, it seems like the least I could do...

But...

Then I don't really have to wear them... just have them.

If Kiriya gave me these because he's serious like Nanri says...

STARE...

DID THAT HURT?
GETTING YOUR EARS PIERCED...

...WHAT?

I DID IT MYSELF AND THE HOLES CAME OUT UNEVEN.

DON'T TRY TO DO IT YOURSELF, OKAY?

OH...

N-NOTHING.

ARE YOU GONNA PIERCE YOUR EARS?

TOO? WHAT TOO?

THAT HURTS TOO, HUH...?

A LITTLE, I GUESS...

YOU COULD GET IT DONE AT THE DOCTOR'S OFFICE--THAT'S PROBABLY YOUR SAFEST BET.

.....

YEAH, HA HA...

LOOK, SEE?

HA HA HA

UH...

I THINK SO...?

HUH?

IS THAT DAD'S?

DOCTOR'S OFFICE? THAT MAKES IT SOUND EVEN *WORSE*...

OOF...

HOW LONG CAN YOU STAY OUT TONIGHT?

I NEED TO BE HOME BY ABOUT NINE...

SORRY...

UM... WELL...

Dad...

OH...

OH, OKAY...

SO WE'VE GOT THREE MORE HOURS. I DON'T THINK WE'VE GOT TIME FOR THE FERRIS WHEEL...

...IS HE MAD?

54

HMM ...

I guess I can't blame him for being frustrated...

There are always so many limits on our time together...

TWO-WAY

OH...

HEY!

NOTICE ANYTHING ...?

I'M WEARING THE PERFUME YOU GAVE ME.

IT'S HARD TO TELL IN THIS CROWD, HUH?

SNIFF

HMM... REALLY?

HEY!

STOP-- KIRIYA!

...THAT TICKLES.

UH...

WHA...?

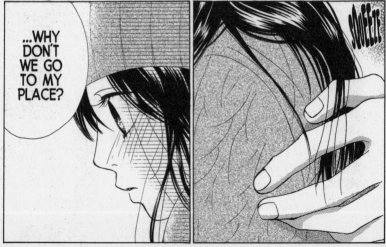

...WHY DON'T WE GO TO MY PLACE?

SQUEEZE

WHAT...?

GRAB

We have sex...!

It's just the two of us...

We go back to Kiriya's...

D-does he mean...?

Gaaaah!!

WE COULD PICK UP WHERE WE LEFT OFF...

ULP

You "don't get it"...?

TRY HARDER!

•••••
GREAT. SHE'S CRY-ING...

THEN...

65

66

RATTLE RATTLE RATTLE

.....

I'M NOT GOING TO LET YOU WALK HOME BY YOURSELF! COME ON!

HEY!

We broke up or anything, but...

It's not like...

I DIDN'T DO ANYTHING WRONG AND I'M NOT GONNA APOLOGIZE!!

Neither one of us said a word on the way home...

MAYBE I SHOULD APOLO-GIZE...?

SAY I WAS WRONG...

I know I don't like fighting with him...

He's acting like he's doing me some huge favor...

Don't people usually wait to have sex until they're both ready?

Why are we always fighting about sex...?

What did he mean, "Do you even know me...?"

But I'm not wrong...!

......

SIGH...

69

DRIVER'S LICENSE
Name: Aoi Kiriya
Birthday: 10/07
Valid until birthday of 10/07/07

4560897006 0

I MISS OKINAWA...

WHEN'D SHE GET SO OBSTINATE...

SHE WAS STILL FUN BACK THEN... WHAT HAPPENED...?

Lens

PHOTO DIVER

Photography Monthly

Kozo Hayashi: Scenes from the Countryside

PhotoTech

THE PHOTO

BOOK FAIR

SHE GETS OUT OF TUTORING SOON. I SHOULD GO PICK HER UP...

IT'S EIGHT O'CLOCK...

THANK YOU.

Photograr Monthly THE 10th

MAYBE I WAS PUSHING A LITTLE...

SO SHOULD I APOLOGIZE? ADMIT I WAS PARTLY TO BLAME? WHAT IF I'M *NOT* SORRY...?

WHAT ARE YOU DOING FOR NEW YEAR'S? ARE YOU COMING HOME?

UM...

NO, I DON'T THINK SO.

KIRIYA?

HELLO?

IT'S SHOKO.

...HEY.

WE ARE IN THE MIDDLE OF A FIGHT... MAYBE I WON'T GO...

.....

DEEDLE DEEDLE

I KNOW...

KIRIYA, YOUR FOLKS KNOW THAT ACCIDENT WASN'T YOUR FAULT.

YOU DON'T HAVE TO STAY AWAY, OKAY?

IS THIS... BECAUSE OF YUJI?

DON'T SAY THAT! THAT'S NOT TRUE.

I'M ALREADY SCHEDULED TO WORK AND I DON'T EXACTLY THINK I'D BE WELCOME...

AND, YOU KNOW, KARIN'S ALWAYS CLAMORING TO SPEND TIME WITH ME, SO--

ROSTLE

GEEZ
...

Photog

I'LL COME HOME IF I FEEL UP TO IT...

Contest
Results

First Prize, Aoi Kiriya (Tokyo, Age 16)
Critique

GASP

Photography
Monthly

THOSE OF YOU WHO PLAN TO CONTINUE OVER THE BREAK...

THIS EVENING MARKS THE END OF OUR REGULAR CURRICULUM, BUT I'D ADVISE YOU NOT TO SLACK OFF DURING WINTER BREAK...

...ENTRANCE EXAMS ARE RIGHT AROUND THE CORNER.

College Prep Classes

New Term
New Term

Enroll
Today

Get into the Uni Of Your Choice

····· 8:30

HE'S LATE...

YEAH... I GUESS.

OH!

WAITING FOR KIRIYA?

HEY! HIROMU, WHY DON'T *YOU* WALK ME HOME?

How annoying...

Kiriya's got me trained!

--NO, IT'S JUST... HABIT.

INERTIA...

REALLY? HE USUALLY COMES TO MEET YOU, SO I THOUGHT--

HEH...

NO, I'M NOT.

THAT PERV...?

WHAT?

WAIT, NO. NO!

We're fighting!

CRUNCH

CLENCH

...how much who you're with affects how you feel...

It's funny...

.....

I guess it takes more than love to make a relationship work...

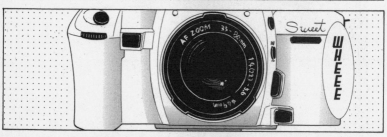

HI, THERE. CAN I HELP YOU? FRIEND OF KIRIYA'S?

YES... OR, I MEAN... WELL, COULD YOU TAKE A LOOK AT THIS?

LET'S HAVE THE KID TAKE A LOOK.

GIVING YOU TROUBLE?

HERE...

THE BATTERIES ARE DEAD.

BEEN A WHILE SINCE YOU USED IT?

ACTUALLY...

YES.

YES.

YOU WORK ON NEW YEAR'S?

.....

OKAY... I'LL SWITCH OUT THE BATTERIES AND DO A QUICK CHECK.

I LIVE ALONE AND DON'T MIND WORKING, SO...

EXCUSE ME, WOULD YOU HAVE TWO...?

WE HAVE THE PERFECT NEW YEAR'S KIMONO FOR YOU. WANNA TRY IT?

NO CHARGE FOR A FRIEND OF KIRIYA'S.

YOU RENT CLOTHES, TOO?

Formal Wear
8000~

Kiriya...

He's still mad...

84

I wonder how long I can take it...

I wonder how long it's gonna be like this...

I wish I knew how to fix it...

WOW! AMAZING WHAT THE RIGHT CLOTHES CAN DO...

YESSIR.

KIRIYA, YOU ALL SET OVER THERE?

·····

THANKS...

CAREFUL ON THE STEPS.

HIS FAMILY'S WELL OFF, BUT HE DOESN'T WANT TO RELY ON THEM. WORKS HARD, SUPPORTS HIMSELF...

DON'T FIND MANY LIKE HIM NOWADAYS...

YES, WELL, AT FIRST HE WAS JUST HELPING OUT HERE AND THERE. THEN, WHEN HIS ELDER BROTHER DIED, HE FELL OUT WITH HIS PARENTS AND MOVED...

I THINK HE WANTED TO STAY BUSY SO THAT HE COULD FORGET WHAT HAPPENED.

HOW... HOW LONG HAS HE WORKED FOR YOU?

ABOUT A YEAR AND A HALF. STARTED IN THE SUMMER OF NINTH GRADE.

NINTH GRADE?

HE REALLY MANAGES TO CAPTURE THE WARMTH HE FEELS FOR HIS SUBJECT...

UH...

WELL...

YOU'RE PRETTY INTERESTED IN KIRIYA.

SOMETHING TO DO WITH THAT YOUNG DAUGHTER OF YOURS?

LOOK AT THAT-- HE TOOK THAT.

ISN'T THAT GREAT?

DON'T WORRY. KID'S GOT A GOOD HEAD ON HIS SHOULDERS.

92

Kiriya...

THAT PHOTO JUST WON FIRST PRIZE IN A CONTEST, MISS.

YES.

RIGHT?

YOUR FIRST BLUE RIBBON...

·····

I've never seen anything like that...

That's what I look like in Kiriya's eyes...

96

WHR

KSHH

Look
at
him...

He's so
happy when
he's got
that camera
in his
hands...

HUH...

WHY DON'T YOU TAKE ONE WITH US THIS TIME?

YOU LET ME DECIDE WHAT'S RIGHT!

IT'S A FAMILY PORTRAIT.

WOULDN'T BE RIGHT!

OH NO, THAT'S ALL RIGHT!

THERE MUST BE SOME REASON WE RAN INTO YOU HERE.

IT'S NEW YEAR'S. WOULD IT KILL YOU TO TAKE *ONE* PICTURE WITH US?

•••••

NO, OF COURSE NOT...

READY? HERE WE GO.

CONGRATU- LATIONS...

...ON THE CONTEST...

THANKS...

S-SORRY.

HEY LOVEBIRDS, DON'T CLOSE YOUR EYES.

HEY, KIRIYA, YOU CAN GO NOW, TOO, IF YOU'D LIKE.

THANKS.

NO TROUBLE AT ALL. THESE WON'T TAKE LONG TO PROCESS. STOP BACK AS SOON AS IT'S CONVENIENT, OKAY?

THANK YOU FOR ALL YOUR TIME...

COULD WE...COULD I TALK TO YOU FOR A MINUTE?

THANK YOU FOR EVERYTHING TODAY, SIR.

HEY...

WAIT A SEC...!

SURE...

IT'LL BE FINE.

DAD?

WHICH IS IT?

I GUESS WE *INTENDED* TO...

WELL TO BE HONEST, WE *STARTED* TO...

WE *ALMOST* DID--BUT WE STOPPED BEFORE WE REALLY DID...!

IT'S COMPLI-CATED...

YES-- NO! I MEAN, NO...

I'M NOT... WELL...

WHAT?

OR, I MEAN, WELL, WE DID AND WE DIDN'T...

NO SIR, I'M NOT!

ARE YOU HAVING SEX WITH MY DAUGHTER?

THAT PREGNANCY TEST REALLY WASN'T KARIN'S, THEN?

NO! NO, I SWEAR.

I WOULD HAVE PUNCHED YOU, YOU KNOW?

SERIOUSLY ?!

.....

WE'RE SOMEWHERE BETWEEN SECOND AND THIRD BASE. SORRY...

SHE'S THE ONLY ONE I WANT TO BE WITH.

...YOU SHOULD COME BY THE HOUSE SOMETIME.

YOU CAN SEE HIM, BUT ONLY ON WEEKENDS. AND IF IT'S LATE, HE'S GOT TO WALK YOU HOME.

DAD...?

110

...I'M SORRY ABOUT THE OTHER DAY.

No, no, not yet...

Not so fast...

If I make this easy, he'll forget and the same thing'll happen again...

WELL, I WAS WRONG, TOO...

UM...

.....

111

112

114

I'M NOT JUST SOME JERKY PERV. I WANT TO HAVE SEX WITH *YOU*—BECAUSE IT'S *YOU*, AND I'M *IN LOVE WITH YOU*.

I DON'T THINK I COULD CHANGE THAT IF I WANTED TO.

I LOVE YOU.

HEY...

I'D FEEL BETTER IF YOU WERE THERE...

DO YOU THINK YOU COULD HELP ME WITH THESE...?

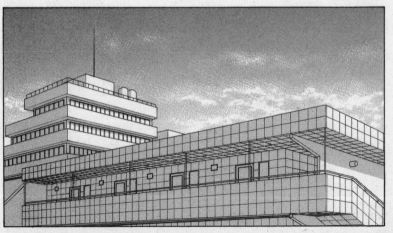

K-
KLITCH

THEY LOOK GOOD ON YOU.

YOU'RE CUTE.

YOU'RE EMBAR-RASSING ME...

IS IT THE DIAMOND? IT'S THE DIAMOND, ISN'T IT?

OH...

.....

That explains it...

...now I under-stand what he meant.

I THINK... APRIL OF LAST YEAR, RIGHT?

SO DO YOU KNOW APRIL'S BIRTH-STONE?

HUH ?

HEY...

DO YOU REMEMBER WHEN IT WAS THAT WE FIRST MET?

120

BUT...I WANT IT TO BE WHEN WE'RE *BOTH* READY...

OTHERWISE, IT'S KIND OF EMPTY, DON'T YOU THINK?

ARE YOU SURE?

I'M JUST KIDDING. I'M THRILLED! THANK YOU.

I'M SURE.

SO...HAVE YOU ALWAYS BEEN SUCH A SAP?

.....

LET'S TAKE A PICTURE FOR POSTERITY.

I LOVE YOU TOO, KIRIYA...

AND WHEN I DO HAVE SEX, I WANT IT TO BE WITH YOU.

YOU KNOW...

123

When I met Kiriya...

I found out what it feels like to love someone.

In the time we've known each other...

I've learned more than I can even put into words...

YOU PIERCED YOUR EARS?

Changes ...

HEH. NOTHING. IT JUST SEEMS LIKE YOU'VE BEEN MAKING A LOT OF CHANGES FOR HIM LATELY, THAT'S ALL.

YEAH, SO...? WHAT ABOUT IT?

I KNOW YOU LOVE HIM BUT, I MEAN, YOU PUT A HOLE IN YOUR OWN BODY. THAT'S PRETTY HUGE, RIGHT?

SERIOUSLY ...?!

HAVE I REALLY ...?

SHOCKING!

YEAH...I GUESS I DIDN'T REALLY THINK OF IT THAT WAY. IT'S NOT LIKE HE *ORDERED* ME TO DO IT OR ANYTHING...

I JUST THOUGHT IT MIGHT MAKE HIM HAPPY. I DUNNO, I GUESS...I WANT TO BE WHAT HE WANTS, YOU KNOW? IT'S HARD TO RESIST.

OH, I KNOW. AND THAT'S NORMAL--ESPECIALLY WHEN YOU'RE ALL STARRY-EYED--BUT I'VE LEARNED FROM EXPERIENCE THAT IT'S BETTER TO MAKE *THEM* CHANGE.

I KNOW, RIGHT? I REALIZED A LOT WHEN I DUMPED THAT LOSER OVER THE WHOLE PREGNANCY THING.

THAT'S SO YOU, NANRI.

HEH. YEAH, THAT DOESN'T SURPRISE ME.

126

FIRST AND FOREMOST... MEN HAVE TO BE *TRAINED*.

THEY HAVE TO BE MODIFIED SO THEY WON'T MAKE ME CRY.

OH... OKAY...

......

We haven't even managed to have sex yet, but...

AS SOON AS YOU HAVE SEX WITH THEM THEY EITHER SHUT DOWN AND TURN COLD, OR THEY GO PATHETIC AND ALL THEY CAN DO IS BEG FOR MORE.

THEY'RE NICE WHEN THEY WANT SOMETHING.

I LIKE KIRIYA, BUT I WANT YOU TO PROMISE YOU WON'T LET YOUR GUARD DOWN, ALL RIGHT?

RECENT FIGHTS

LET'S GO TO A HOTEL!

IF YOU WON'T GO ALL THE WAY THEN DON'T EVEN START!

THIS SOUNDS FAMILIAR...

I PROMISE I'LL BE CAREFUL.

GOOD.

......

Oh, Nanri...

I JUST DON'T WANT YOU TO MAKE THE SAME MISTAKE I DID.

EVERY-THING'S GOING SO WELL FOR YOU GUYS, AND I WANT IT TO STAY THAT WAY...

OH?

ANYWAY. I'VE BEEN THINKING ABOUT HIROMU LATELY...

WELL, YOU SOUND LIKE YOU'RE DOING ALL RIGHT, NANRI...

I'M GLAD...

KARIN, I THINK YOU SHOULD START KIRIYA'S TRAINING *IMMEDIATELY.*

YEAH, ♪OKAY...

IT'S NOT GOING TO BE EASY TO GET HIS ATTENTION.

I LIKE A CHAL-LENGE.

DO YOU...?

IT'S NOT SERIOUS. HE'S INTO ACADEMICS.. REALLY INEXPERIENCED WITH GIRLS. I THINK THAT MIGHT MAKE HIM A GOOD TRAINEE...

I KNEW YOU SAW EACH OTHER OVER CHRISTMAS, BUT I DIDN'T THINK...

128

You won't shut me out as soon as we have sex, will you...?

WHAT WERE YOU THINKING JUST NOW?

UM...I WAS THINKING ABOUT YOU.

SO ARE YOU.

OH!... YOU'RE BLUSH-ING.

I DIDN'T THINK ANYTHING!

OH HEY, ARE YOU GONNA BE AROUND THIS SATURDAY?

BESIDES, I WANT TO TAKE ADVANTAGE OF OUR NEW NO-CURFEW WEEKENDS. THINK YOUR DAD WOULD BE COOL WITH IT?

YOU'RE SCARED OF MY DAD, AREN'T YOU?

HEE HEE

WELL, HE'S SCARY, RIGHT?!

I GUESS. HEE HEE.

I COULD TAKE SOME MORE PICTURES OF YOU WHILE WE'RE UP THERE.

SHOKO INVITED ME TO SIT IN ON A PHOTO SHOOT. THE PHOTOGRAPHER'S REALLY COOL.

IT'S WAY UP IN THE MOUNTAINS, BUT YOU SHOULD COME IF YOU'RE NOT BUSY.

132

YOUR HANDS ARE FREEZING.

HEY...

SLIP

THAT'S OKAY. IT'S ALWAYS LIKE THIS ON THE WEEK-ENDS. ANY-WAY, I'M USED TO STANDING ON THE MORNING BUS.

I'M SORRY WE COULDN'T FIND SEATS.

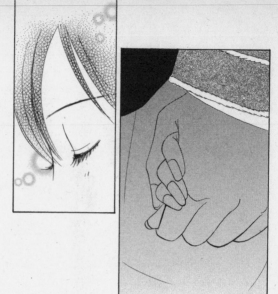

YOUR HANDS ARE COLD TOO, KIRIYA...

THERE.

OKAY.

ALL RIGHT, IF WE'RE GOING TO GET THERE BY THREE, WE SHOULD HEAD TO THE BUS STOP.

Oumeizan-Nikko Station

	UP		DOWN
6		6	
7	52	7	
8		8	
9		9	10
10	15	10	
11		11	
12		12	
13	30	13	44
14		14	

OH, MAN...

AND WE'RE GOING TO THE LAST STOP, RIGHT?

THE BUS SCHEDULE THAT SHOKO SENT US IS OUT-OF-DATE.

...THREE HOURS.

WHAAAT?!

Schedule
Mountain
se

44

30

59 m

32

Bus runs every 3 hours.

HOW LONG TILL THE NEXT ONE?

WE JUST MISSED IT...

Schedule
Mountain
e Station

.....

BUS STOP
umeizan
Line

BUT YOU CAN WALK TO THE LAST STATION.

IT'S NOT THAT FAR.

THAT SCHEDULE JUST RECENTLY CHANGED.

I GUESS WE HAVE NO CHOICE. WHAT DO YOU THINK?

BETTER THAN WAITING THREE HOURS...

MAYBE "IT'S NOT THAT FAR" ACTUALLY MEANS, "I'M GOING TO PLAY A FUNNY JOKE ON THE TOURISTS."

HEH...

MAYBE SO...

...AT LEAST THE FLOWERS ARE PRETTY.

DRIP

DRIP

I actually don't mind this. It's nice to be alone together...

LET'S JUST ENJOY THE SCENERY?

OKAY?

141

YEAH...

OKAY, I GUESS...

WELL... AT LEAST WE CAN DRY OFF AND CALL SHOKO...

SQUEEZE

144

SHOKO? IT'S ME.

.....

.....

UM... APPARENTLY THERE'S A BIG STORM UP THE MOUNTAIN.

THE BUSES AREN'T EVEN RUNNING...

OH? SO...

YEAH, UM...

.....

KARIN...

Y-YES?

146

147

No Service

OKAY...

THANKS.

USE MINE.

•••••

•••••

NO DIAL TONE...

OH, RIGHT.

HA HA HA

OH YEAH, WE CAN USE THE LAND LINE.

DUH.

SURE.

UM... ARE YOU HUNGRY?

I GUESS SO.

I GUESS SO.

IT MUST BE SOME STORM... WE JUST HAVE TO SIT TIGHT FOR A WHILE.

NO, I... I'M GONNA KEEP TRYING MY CELL PHONE...

YOU SHOULD TAKE ONE FIRST. YOU'LL CATCH A COLD.

WHY DON'T I GO SEE WHAT THERE IS TO EAT WHILE YOU TAKE A SHOWER AND GET WARMED UP.

SHINJI... TAKAGI?

THE PHOTO- GRAPHER?

OH!

This must be the guy Kiriya was telling me about.

157

AH...

IF ONLY YOU WERE FIVE OR SIX YEARS OLDER...

TOO BAD.

HUH?!

YOU'RE HURT. YOU SHOULD LET ME CARRY YOU TO THE CAR.

THAT'S OKAY-- REALLY! I'M NOT HURT THAT BAD.

I-I BEG YOUR PARDON...?

COULD YOU PUT ME DOWN NOW?

GRAB

158

I'LL TAKE HER.

DROP

!!

SURE...

CATCH!

I'M KIDDING. I'M KIDDING.

ER...

HA HA HA!

SORRY.

YOU DIDN'T THINK THAT WAS FUNNY?

SHINJI, QUIT MESSING AROUND AND GET IN THE CAR!

What is this guy's deal?!

HE'S FREAKING ME OUT...

I'M GLAD WE FOUND YOU GUYS.

HA HA!

YEAH...

THANKS.

I IMAGINE IT WOULD HAVE BEEN AWKWARD STAYING AT "HOTEL L'AMOUR," HUH?

WE'LL TAKE YOU TO OUR HOTEL, DON'T WORRY.

SHINJI WAS A BUDDY OF YUJI'S, KIRIYA...

NICE TO MEET YOU.

OH! THIS IS SHINJI TAKAGI... IT'S HIS SHOOT.

HE KNEW MY BROTHER...

NO, I SHOULD CALL.

I SHOULD CALL KARIN'S FOLKS AND LET THEM KNOW WHAT'S GOING ON.

YOU SURE ABOUT THAT...?

TANIMOTO HOTEL

HER FOLKS DON'T HAVE ANY REASON NOT TO TRUST ME...

YOU THINK THEY'RE GOING TO BE COMFORTABLE KNOWING SHE'S SPENDING THE NIGHT WITH HER BOYFRIEND?

BETTER LET ONE OF US CALL SO THEY KNOW SHE'S WITH AN ADULT.

THEY WERE BOTH ASSISTANTS FOR THE SAME PHOTO- GRAPHER, WAY BACK WHEN.

WHILE YOU GET SHINJI TO TELL YOU SOME STORIES ABOUT YUJI, OKAY?

LOOK, IT DOESN'T MATTER. I'LL CALL...

OH...?

162

RIIIIGHT.

I'M PSYCHIC.

HEH HEH

H-HOW DID YOU KNOW THAT?

HUH?

LET ME GUESS... YOUR BIRTHDAY IS IN APRIL, RIGHT?

KARIN! SHOKO GOT US A ROOM.

OH, OKAY.

TINK

WELL... GOOD NIGHT.

ISN'T APRIL'S BIRTHSTONE A DIAMOND?

•••••

...I never found my earring!

Oh yeah...

'NIGHT.

?

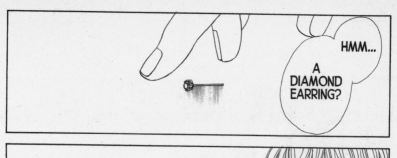

HMM... A DIAMOND EARRING?

WHAT'S UP? DIDN'T YOU LIKE HIM? YOU LOOK KIND OF GLOOMY...

YEAH... I DIDN'T THINK HE WOULD BE SO FRIENDLY.

SINCE HE'S FAMOUS AND ALL...

HE'S NOT QUITE WHAT I WAS EXPECTING, YOU KNOW?

HUH?

HEY! WHAT JUST HAPPENED?

NEVER MIND.

FORGET IT.

HERE, THIS IS THE KEY TO YOUR ROOM.

CARD KEY

TANIMOTO HOTEL

.....

YOU GUYS HAVE BEEN GOING OUT FOR A YEAR NOW. I FIGURE YOU KNOW YOUR OWN LIMITS, RIGHT?

THIS IS OKAY, ISN'T IT?

I THOUGHT ABOUT HAVING KARIN STAY IN MY ROOM, BUT I DIDN'T WANT TO BE A PRUDE...

UH...

WELL, THERE'S ONLY ONE ROOM.

THERE'S ONLY ONE...?

WHAT DOES THAT MEAN?

SURE, OF COURSE.

RIGHT, KIRIYA?

I CAN TRUST YOU, HUH?

.....

OKAY THEN, GOOD NIGHT!

Whew!

JUST KILL ME...

I SHOULD HAVE KNOWN ...

He's so quiet. Should I say something ...?

Hmm...

Get changed ...?

WE SHOULD DO SOMETHING ABOUT YOUR LEG, HUH?

YEAH ...

WHY DON'T YOU TAKE A SHOWER AND GET CHANGED? YOU'RE SOAKED.

I'M GONNA ASK THE FRONT DESK IF THEY HAVE ANYTHING TO PUT ON IT...

GOOD IDEA, THANKS.

All there is.

Haven't we already been through this...?

OH, MAN...

I should just get it over with...

Maybe... I just need to get warmed up— like at Christmas...

Kiriya's been so patient...

.....

YEAH, IT DOES. HE MUST ADMIRE HIS WORK... AND WHEN HE DOES TURN PRO, LIKE IT OR NOT, HE'S GOING TO BE COMPARED TO HIS BROTHER.

SERIOUSLY?

I REALLY LIKE HIS STUFF. DOES IT LOOK *THAT* MUCH LIKE YUJI?

My earring...

Should I just tell him that I lost it...?

I CAN'T...

HE WORKED SO HARD...

SLAM

.....

TA DA!

These things...

...are not exactly flattering...

I LOOK LIKE A SACK.

UM...

KIRI...

PLOP

175

SO YOU TWO ARE ON A FIRST NAME BASIS ALREADY?

HUH?

I HAVE NEVER ONCE HEARD YOU CALL ME "AOI."

DO YOU HAVE THE HOTS FOR THAT GUY OR SOMETHING?

YOU NEVER CALL *ME* BY MY FIRST NAME.

I MEAN, HE'S RICH, RIGHT?

HE DRIVES A LUXURY CAR.

A WHAT?

WHAT IS YOUR PROBLEM? WHERE IS THIS COMING FROM?

YOU RAN OFF BEFORE BECAUSE YOU DIDN'T WANNA BE ALONE WITH ME-- DIDN'T YOU?!

N-NO... THAT WAS...

W-WHOA...

WHERE DID *THAT* COME FROM? HE TOLD ME TO CALL HIM BY HIS FIRST NAME, SO THAT'S WHAT I DID.

YOU'RE JUST GONNA DO WHATEVER HE TELLS YOU...

178

FLIP

BE
CAREFUL
WHAT
YOU START,
KARIN...

Kare First Love 5 End.

The Power of a Kiss

Soon after her first kiss, Yuri is pulled into a puddle and transported to an ancient Middle Eastern village. Surrounded by strange people speaking a language she can't understand, Yuri has no idea how to get back home and is soon embroiled in the politics and romance of the ancient Middle East. If a kiss helped get Yuri into this mess, can a kiss get her out?

RED RIVER

Start your graphic novel collection today!

ONLY $9.95!

www.viz.com
store.viz.com

LOVE SHOJO? LET US KNOW!

☐ Please do NOT send me information about VIZ Media products, news and events, special offers, or other information.

☐ Please do NOT send me information from VIZ' trusted business partners.

Name: _____

Address: _____

City: _____ State: _____ Zip: _____

E-mail: _____

☐ Male ☐ Female Date of Birth (mm/dd/yyyy): ___/___/___ (Under 13? Parental consent required)

What race/ethnicity do you consider yourself? (check all that apply)

☐ White/Caucasian   ☐ Black/African American   ☐ Hispanic/Latino

☐ Asian/Pacific Islander ☐ Native American/Alaskan Native ☐ Other: _____

What VIZ shojo title(s) did you purchase? (indicate title(s) purchased)

_____

What other shojo titles from other publishers do you own? _____

_____

Reason for purchase: (check all that apply)

☐ Special offer   ☐ Favorite title / author / artist / genre

☐ Gift   ☐ Recommendation   ☐ Collection

☐ Read excerpt in VIZ manga sampler   ☐ Other _____

Where did you make your purchase? (please check one)

☐ Comic store   ☐ Bookstore   ☐ Mass/Grocery Store

☐ Newsstand   ☐ Video/Video Game Store

☐ Online (site:_____) ☐ Other _____

How many shojo titles have you purchased in the last year? How many were VIZ shojo titles?
(please check one from each column)

SHOJO MANGA

☐ None
☐ 1 – 4
☐ 5 – 10
☐ 11+

VIZ SHOJO MANGA

☐ None
☐ 1 – 4
☐ 5 – 10
☐ 11+

What do you like most about shojo graphic novels? (check all that apply)

☐ Romance
☐ Comedy
☐ Other _____

☐ Drama / conflict
☐ Real-life storylines

☐ Fantasy
☐ Relatable characters

Do you purchase every volume of your favorite shojo series?

☐ Yes! Gotta have 'em as my own
☐ No. Please explain: _____

Who are your favorite shojo authors / artists? _____

_____

What shojo titles would like you translated and sold in English? _____

_____

THANK YOU! Please send the completed form to:

NJW Research
ATTN: VIZ Media Shojo Survey
42 Catharine Street
Poughkeepsie, NY 12601